FUN THI

to do while you

SIT ON THE LOO

CW00765348

K.Murdle

Published by Kent Publishers

ISBN: 9798988689522

Printed and Shipped From U.S

First Edition: Oct, 2023

Want a quirky twist for your restroom? Get your favorite pages transformed into a merch poster for your bathroom! Send an email to murdlepooper@gmail.com

odd tidbits from the world of bathrooms

Ancient Cleaning: *Before toilet paper was a thing, ancient Romans used a sponge-on-a-stick called a "tersorium" to clean themselves post-business. After use, it was plunged back into a bucket of salt water.*

World's Most Expensive Bathroom: *Estimated to be worth over $29 million, a bathroom in Hong Kong has gold and jewel-encrusted toilets and washbasins.*

Musical Toilets: *In Japan, some toilets have a noise button that plays music or a flushing sound to mask any unwanted noises. This is for those who're a tad shy about letting nature be heard.*

Sitting vs. Squatting: *The debate over which is healthier, sitting or squatting, continues. Some health experts argue that squatting is more natural and better for digestive health.*

Pay to Pee: *In parts of Europe, you'll come across public toilets that require payment. Some of these "pay-per-pee" facilities even have attendants to ensure the fee is collected.*

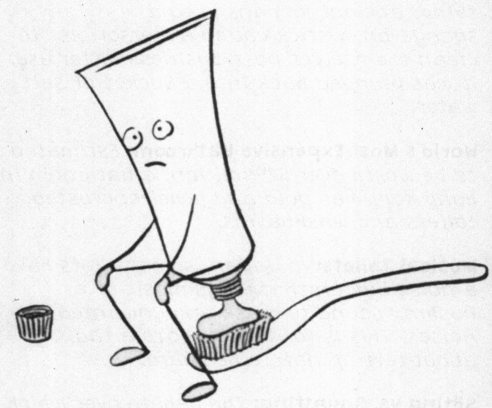

What's the worst thing someone can do in the bathroom?

Mistake the toilet brush for a toothbrush.

Life Lesson
From A Roll of Toilet Paper

LIFE...

is like

TOILET PAPER

You're either

ON A ROLL

or taking

Crap

FROM

SOMEONE

Why can't farts get a decent education?
Because they always get expelled.

Help The Farting Pig Get to The Toilet
(before he poops on himself)

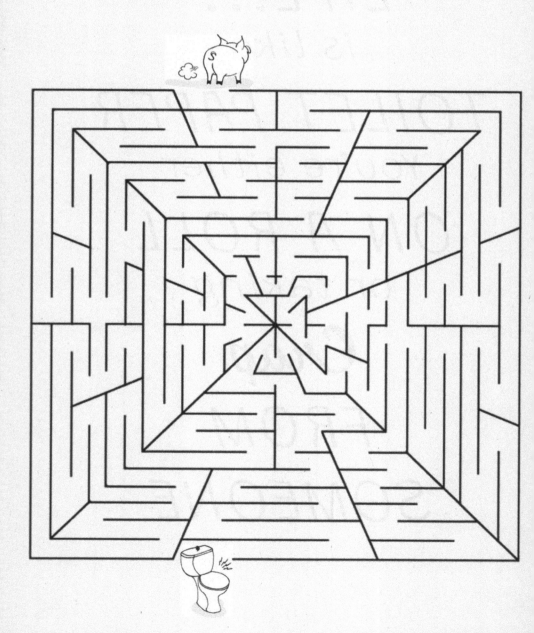

KNOCK KNOCK! JOKES

Knock-knock!
Who's there?
Ooze.
Ooze who?

Ooze gonna clean up this toilet?

Knock-knock!
Who's there?
Watt.
Watt who?

Watt died in here?

Word Search

Brain While You Drain

```
C E R G F R Y V B D S L M F U O Q G E O
D V J R E V E B U G H H L I K T E E H E
C C F R J T H W G G H K E W K W V W V K
O X N T E I S P O K E L J D L U A B K U
I U B I X S Y A N P Q K W I A D F I R P
X T S S P D N W P X M G I T D T B O C I
R R O S U U E E K H G U X H A Y M X O E
V C A U W E H L P H T T C E S K W J O F
V A P E B U O K S S E O S L O T Q V Z S
W Q D S I G G U S L I T O M A R G F U C
S G I F T G R W I F E D M T P T L B L Z
C K S A P B A O I L G Q P K W J U O E J
O Q H F H B T K I W J N W A D P O A T C
S C G T S F V O V X T P Q Q O O M J Y G
Q G O E Q P T O N E A F U E I S R W I P
O O H L F M H C J F R S P O N G E V Y Z
T R M S N U Y N Q C Z F H J M N O I Y H
R A V I T O I L E T P A P E R J N H V H
I N B L J J I F X U B K W M K N G L M J S
C D H J R D B M U Q M A N K A R C B R J
```

Word List

SOAP	SOAP DISH	SOAP DISPENSER
SPONGE	SWABS	TALCUM POWER
TISSUES	TOILET	TOILET PAPER
TOILET SEAT	TOOTHBRUSH	TOOTHPASTE

Why shouldn't you fart in an Apple store? *They don't have Windows.*

Wombats Have Cube Shaped Poop

Sudok-Poo!

	9			8	1	7		2
6		7	5		4	1	8	
2		8	6	7			5	4
		1						7
4								
	8		9	3		4	1	
		9						
1					5			
	4		1	6		9	7	

Did you hear about the movie Constipation?

It was never released.

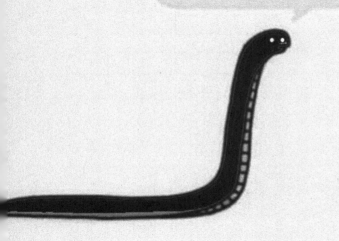

Word Scramble

Brain While You Drain

What's the only TV show you can watch in the bathroom?
Game of Thrones.

BATHROOM

RIAEENPNL

CESENODN

NNITNTONIEC

REPBULM

POYTT

OCNPUDMO

NNDDINETEPE

ODEUCLC

EBEIDECON

RIHTSET

AEASDNMARL

EMOLMZIIBI

"Fart for freedom, fart for liberty—and fart proudly."

— BENJAMIN FRANKLIN

Mindfulness

silently bringing in the breeze and mindfully releasing the sneeze!

INHALE

EXHALE

Connect the Plops

Just remember, every dot (and toot) counts!

deja poo

| dey - zhah : poo | adj.

the feeling that you went through this exact same crap yesterday.

BATHROOM LEGALITIES

Whistling in the Loo (Scotland): Allegedly, in Scotland, it was once illegal to whistle in a public bathroom. The belief was that it could summon evil spirits.

Flushing After Certain Hours (Switzerland): In some apartment buildings in Switzerland, residents are discouraged or supposedly prohibited from flushing the toilet after 10 PM as it's considered noise pollution.

No Snakes in the Toilet (Australia): In Queensland, there's a law that prohibits pet snakes from being in a position where they could enter toilets used by the public or neighbors. This was after incidents of snakes appearing in toilets became more common.

Public Toilet Usage Fee (Many European countries): Not so much a "crazy" legality, but visitors from other parts of the world might find it unusual that many public toilets charge a fee for usage.

Same Building, Different Facilities (Alabama, USA): In Alabama, it's supposedly illegal to have two toilets installed in the same building unless they're in separate rooms.

A poop is just a fart that worked hard and applied itself.

Connect the Plops

Just remember, every dot (and toot) counts!

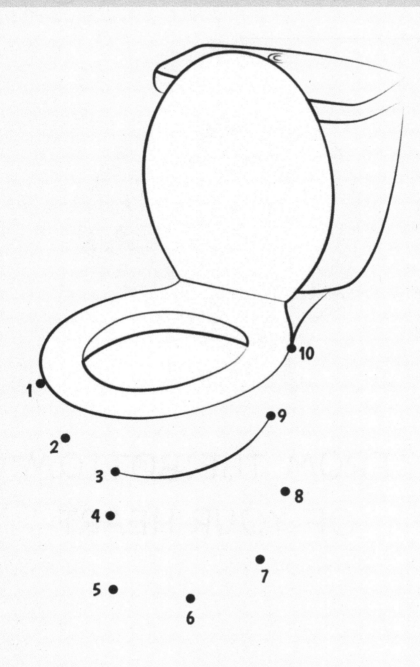

FROM THE BOTTOM
OF YOUR HEART

KNOCK KNOCK!

Knock-knock!
Who's there?
Noah.
Noah who?

*Noah where the bathroom is?
I'm about to blow!*

Knock-knock!
Who's there?
Abbott.
Abbott who?

*Abbott time we got a
candle for this bathroom!*

You Have To Roll With What Life Gives You.

Did you hear about the guy who got lost in the bathroom?

He took a wrong turd.

Help the turd to the toilet!

Mindfulness

silently bringing in the breeze and mindfully releasing the sneeze!

INHALE

EXHALE

Why shouldn't you take Pokémon into the bathroom when you need to go? They might Pikachu.

```
C H A J E E D G O Y B F O B
P L X P S F L O A T E R S O
A E Z A O K G D Y D P I N O
B R E Y U O E L Z O I S W L
G T O W G I P P Y O D J E Y
R E W S A M H I W D U C T I
O T Q E G U Y S E O S P S V
S I R K E E M S X O F S E T
S G U P A W Y T C A U T A V
D Y R S Q E E W R S K U T A
Q U I N T S F E A R I N L N
U C N O Y I J G P B A K E Y
R K E H E V N S H I T N P A
I Y O U S S O K C M S J T H
```

PEE	POOP	STINK
PISS	SHIT	STUNK
URINE	CRAP	GROSS
WEEWEE	DOODOO	YUCKY
WETSEAT	FLOATERS	GAG

*If you complete this search in one visit consult physician.

Squeeze

MY BOTTOM

Sudok-Poo!

Ensuring no 'number repeats' in this gassy grid

3			7					
7					6	2		4
6				2			1	3
9		6		3				5
			2					9
4	3				5			1
1	9				7	3		
		8		9			4	6

What's the biggest toilet in the world?

The Super Bowl.

YOU MUST BE NEW HERE...

Word Scramble

Brain While You Drain

Why did the woman put plastic wrap on the toilet seat?

She wanted to seal in the freshness

WOMEN

POASNOR

OIXLLPB

CCTRMIALIEC

BRTUNA

IATOXEMNF

LDEDDI

BNIELAS

EAHRTCSMO

NSAIUM

ENIEGRC

SHALW

HIHSSEWR

odd tidbits from the world of bathrooms

Toilet Spirits: *In ancient Japan, it was believed that a ghost named "Aka Manto" haunted public restrooms and would ask you if you wanted red or blue toilet paper. Choosing either option could lead to dire consequences!*

World Toilet Day: *November 19th is officially recognized as World Toilet Day. It aims to raise awareness about the 2.5 billion people who don't have access to basic sanitation.*

Loo Learning: *The average person spends about 1 to 1.5 years of their life in the bathroom. That's a lot of time! You could read a good chunk of an encyclopedia in that* **span!**

Royal Reading: *King Henry VIII of England had a 'Groom of the Stool,' whose duty it was to chat with the king while he was on the toilet and, well, help him get cleaned up afterward. Now that's a crappy job!*

Word Search

Brain While You Drain

```
C Q V S C U O F Y C S Z K G J W P K I K
Q L Z O L K B Q U R X H V E B E J R A D
A D Q H L J A A F W F X M F X B W G R Y
E K P J K P D J R B O G M O J O C H R I
H G O G Q R D E T U W R P C N R B U F D
M Z X N S G Z D R O C C H J B H Z U R M
C M B O L I F O B B K Q O R W T C S F D
P T J D M R E N N Z A E U F B A B K D G
E S U O R B S Z H J H S P S L B M T J N
F Y T S Q S C R C F H A I N O X O A Z G
D A D Z T Z K D S I R R T N I T F D E E
A R Y G I D L A X W T E F I T P R O I A
U C B A T H M A T N D P J Y Q X B T Y L
B A T H T U B S I I Y L E X Y A S F R M
N W P G S F U R B R Y Z A S N V M W Q G
J M A B M D I Z G Q Q Z S D I P U L V O
L I A D O P D D O D F R A S X T Q X V L
V T R X S R D X O P U G G Z A A N S N G
H C B A R Y L G W M E W N Y C C N A U B
B A T H T O W E L S Z U X G J N F Z K E
```

Word List

ANTISEPTIC	ASPIRIN	ATOMIZER
BANDAGES	BASIN	BATH
BATH MAT	BATH TOWEL	BATHROBE
BATHTUB	BIDET	BRUSH

Why did the bum interrupt the speech?
Because he liked to butt in.

BATHROOM LEGALITIES

Only For Customers (California, USA): *Many places in California and other parts of the U.S. have signs stating restrooms are for customers only, due to business laws and limited facilities.*

No Lions in the Bathtub (Baltimore, Maryland, USA): *A peculiar and likely outdated law, it is said to be illegal to take a lion into the movies or to have one in your bathtub.*

Singing in the Tub (Pennsylvania, USA): *Rumor has it that it's against the law to sing in the bathtub in Pennsylvania.*

Gender Restrictions (Several Countries): *In some countries, there are strict laws about which genders can enter certain restrooms, especially in places of worship or traditional areas.*

Toilet Paper Orientation (Various Myths): *There are jokes and myths that certain places have laws about whether toilet paper should roll over or under. While it's a popular debate, no actual laws dictate this.*

No Ugly Faces (Oklahoma, USA): *This one is more of an urban legend, but it's often shared that in Oklahoma, it's illegal to make ugly faces at a dog, including when you're in a bathroom.*

Farting while you're eating is just a "coming attraction."

Connect the Plops

Just remember, every dot (and toot) counts!

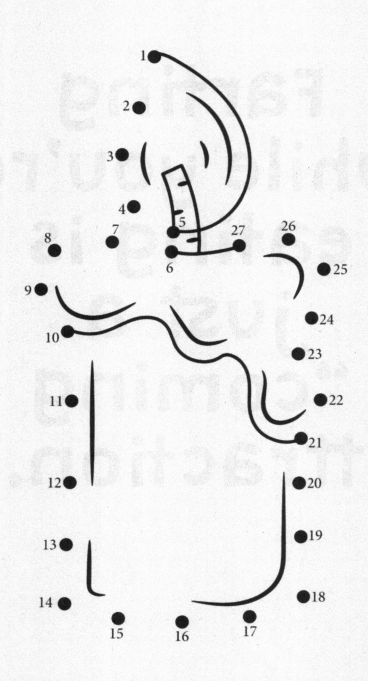

"Everybody looks at their poop."

—OPRAH WINFREY

KNOCK KNOCK!

Knock-knock!
Who's there?
Dewey.
Dewey who?

Dewey really have to share this bathroom?

Knock-knock!
Who's there?
Candice.
Candice who?

Candice bathroom smell any worse?

Life Lesson
From A Roll of Toilet Paper

The Worst Jobs Involve a Lot of Paperwork

What's the grossest device to listen to music with?
An iPood.

Mindfulness

silently bringing in the breeze and mindfully releasing the sneeze!

INHALE

EXHALE

Where's the best place to buy toilet paper? Just find it on Poo-gle.

- WORD SEARCH -

```
A P A S H A R D I T E V E N K A T X S O A F
P O W D E R A K U C P O M S O H V O B M I L
W O K E A M P A I R L A E D R E T A U N T O
M P L O T N M L B E O R B O W L O R B L A S
O B I D E T E F X W I A N P M B O N R E L S
P L R O O P H E P O T E H A E I T S A W O P
S T A R P C A U T H A W L S H S H T U O M O
L O M A U S S R R S H O T E U P R A P T N M
I N S N K E A O E A E A U R L R O M K K A N
D E O T L O O P R A Z A B H A U B I N U H E
M U O B T M A E L P N O O R H X A R O T A Q
A L B U X L N O E U A E R E P A P R O A F K
P U S O R A V B K H S A W D J W A O B X O A
B H E A E P E L P O I L N M F I T R P A O P
Y T E L I O T E A N G R A V O L I N U O L S
A Y C L O D R P L U N G E R A L N I B M E A
```

BATHROOM	FLOSS	POWDER	TOWEL
BIDET	LOOFAH	RAZOR	TUB
BOWL	MIRROR	SHOWER	TUSHY
BRUSH	MOP	SOAP	WASH
BUBBLES	MOUTH	SPA	WAX
CLEANER	PLUNGER	THRONE	
DEODORANT	POOP	TOILET	

Search n Find

I Spy with my brown eye!

Sudok-Poo!

	9			8	1	7		2
6		7	5		4	1	8	
2		8	6	7			5	4
		1						7
4								
	8		9	3		4	1	
		9						
1					5			
	4		1	6		9	7	

Did you hear about the movie Constipation?

It was never released.

DON'T BE ASHAMED
TO FART
WHILE PEEING

REMEMBER,
RAIN
SOMETIMES COMES WITH
THUNDER

odd tidbits from the world of bathrooms

Royal Flush: *King George II of England died from a fall off a toilet in 1760. It's certainly not the most dignified way to go for a monarch!*

Toilet Paper Direction Debate: *The age-old debate of "over vs. under" in toilet paper hanging has been so intense that there are actual patents from the late 1800s showing the "correct" way is "over."*

The Gold Toilet: *The Guggenheim Museum in New York once had an 18-karat gold toilet named "America" that visitors could actually use. Talk about flushing money down the drain!*

Toilet Training: *Historical records suggest that Roman soldiers, during their conquests, sometimes had to attend lessons on how to use the Roman-style toilets.*

Space Potties: *Astronauts use specially designed toilets in space. Due to zero gravity, they need foot straps and thigh braces to keep them secured on the toilet!*

Word Scramble

Brain While You Drain

Why did the woman put plastic wrap on the toilet seat?

She wanted to seal in the freshness

WOMEN

POASNOR ⬜⬜⬜⬜⬜⬜⬜

OIXLLPB ⬜⬜⬜⬜⬜⬜⬜

CCTRMIALIEC ⬜⬜⬜⬜⬜⬜⬜⬜⬜⬜⬜

BRTUNA ⬜⬜⬜⬜⬜⬜

IATOXEMNF ⬜⬜⬜⬜⬜⬜⬜⬜⬜

LDEDDI ⬜⬜⬜⬜⬜⬜

BNIELAS ⬜⬜⬜⬜⬜⬜⬜

EAHRTCSMO ⬜⬜⬜⬜⬜⬜⬜⬜⬜

NSAIUM ⬜⬜⬜⬜⬜⬜

ENIEGRC ⬜⬜⬜⬜⬜⬜⬜

SHALW ⬜⬜⬜⬜⬜

HIHSSEWR ⬜⬜⬜⬜⬜⬜⬜⬜

Word Search

Brain While You Drain

```
Q F A S Q T N B Y F S M Y L G R Y Y U G
X G F R Z O B U B B L E S L R R J W E N
O P A E L R D U D L C O I S P Q A B Z I
C F I P M C W I Z G E U S C D N H S C N
H F A P A W W C S P U O R U G T U E A A
E F W O F W Y E S I L S Y L A W Q I S E
T J R R D U W R Z F N R U B E L W L F L
A U U D R N I A L B S F E D P R L A C C
C H G C E Y B A G G H L E Z M A S O X J
K U F K G L T O N L B S X C B C L D L Y
T J R W A N D K O B A O J N T O U L R Z
X T V L E V R R U I S E O W G A W R I J
P S Z D I Z H B T G U T W N K K N H C L
O O D F V N X J K I T R E K O Z B T J O
P P V Z A Y G Q B O H V A S Q M G W G Y
V G H T F R H I C J T K E U O C P T E N
I D A Y Y W I L R F D P L C L Z J T R B
T T U U Y C A V M O N G Z J Z H S G F A
N G R E N O I T I D N O C I B X G O P I
B A B D B J R X Z L L Z I R D P T B J D
```

Word List

BUBBLE BATH	BUBBLES	CLEANING
COLOGNE	COMB	CONDITIONER
COTTON BALLS	CURLERS	CURLING IRON
DENTAL FLOSS	DISINFECTANT	DROPPERS

Did you hear the joke about squirrel poop? *It was really nutty.*

What kind of toilets can you buy at a drugstore?

Toilet-trees.

BATHROOM ANAGRAM

Minutes and hours   **EXAMPLE**   A thing on a list

TIME ———— **MEIT** ———— **ITEM**

1   A sour fruit   A juicy fruit

———— **ONLME** ————

2   Something you bake   Hair on your face

———— **RDBEA** ————

3   Trees with cones   Synonym for Backbone

———— **SIENP** ————

4   A place to wash dishes   What covers your body

———— **IKNS** ————

5   People wear it in winter   Where land meets sea

———— **TAOSC** ————

6   A piece of beef   A shoe for ice

———— **TAESK** ————

7   A seasoning   The opposite of first

———— **TLAS** ————

8   Synonym for gift   Large snake or dragon

———— **PSTNERE** ————

1. LEMON/MELON   3. PINES/SPINE   5. COATS/COAST   7. SALT/LAST
2. BREAD/BEARD   4. SINK/SKIN   6. STEAK/SKATE   8. PRESENT/SERPENT

Farting is playing a high-stakes game of Chicken with a poop.

Connect the Plops

Just remember, every dot (and toot) counts!

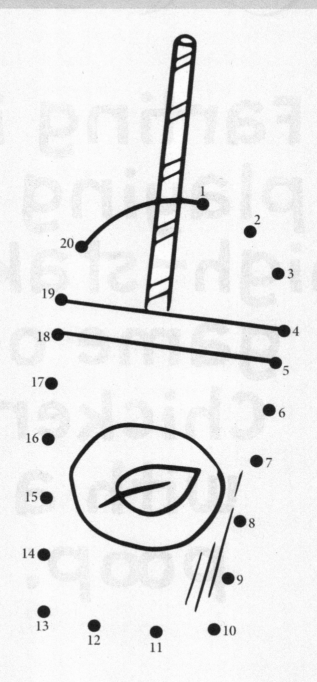

"*Always go to the bathroom when you have a chance.*"

-KING GEORGE V

KNOCK KNOCK! JOKES

Knock-knock!
Who's there?
Donna.
Donna who?

Donna forget to flush when you're done in there!

Knock-knock!
Who's there?
Anita.
Anita who?

Anita go to the bathroom, now!

Be patient when you are learning something new, it's always hardest at first crack.

What does the Pope do in the bathroom?

Holy crap.

Help The Tissue Get to The Butt

Mindfulness

silently bringing in the breeze and mindfully releasing the sneeze!

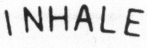

What kind of pizza smells like farts? Poop-eroni.

Search n Find

SOME COME
TO *sit & think*
OTHERS COME
TO JUST
shit & stink

Sudok-Poo!

Ensuring no 'number repeats' in this gassy grid

7					5	1		
				3	6			
		4		8			7	
		7				4	9	
	5	9				3	8	
	3	4				5		
	2		5		9			
			3	4				
		6	2					1

What do you call the guy who has to clean up after the animals?

A pookeeper.

odd tidbits from the world of bathrooms

VIP (Very Important Potty): *The International Space Station's toilet costs about $19 million. That's some space-age splurging!*

Speedy Business: *The average person spends three whole years of their life sitting on the toilet. Hope you brought a good book!*

TP Trivia: *Did you know that 75% of people prefer their toilet paper to come over the roll rather than under? The other 25%? Clearly, they like to live on the edge!*

Ancient TP Alternatives: *Before the invention of toilet paper, humans used various, often quirky materials for that essential cleanup, including wool, lace, and even the classic corn cob!*

Blue Bloods' Bathrooms: *Buckingham Palace has 78 bathrooms. That's one for every eventuality – or for when the Queen's corgis need a quick pit stop!*

Cats' Lavatory Preferences: *Some cat owners swear their feline friends have shown a preference for flushing the toilet. Cats: 1, Toilet Paper Over-Under Debate: 0.*

When Poop is so hard

USE THE FORCE

Word Scramble

Brain While You Drain

Why do horses fart when they gallop?
They wouldn't achieve full horsepower if they didn't.

CHARGING

RJAINUAOTD

GSAOERT

EDWGE

AMNEGIATRRN

TNNTEIMICD

GRATIS

OGEUG

LPEE

IRDFT

DAEL

TAOFGEO

PXEENIVES

Word Search

Brain While You Drain

```
R W M E W L M B W D P C Q B O R V N N P
S H C O I G J E T L W D M C E Y M O X T
G T N N U V Q I D M Q K P P I L O M V N
M X U S J T K P E I C I M A B G J Q F R
A C F W V Z H D S I C A J I R M D P V Z
K R P Y T T I W C H A U Z A O J E U K
E S P K V C H B A Y N S T V P C P W Z T
U G H C I B J D R S U G P I V Y S Q J N
P Y M N V I O D L O H C D S O O D Y S V
Q F E J L T N P J P B E D V B N K F R U
M O I S T U R I Z E R S W A H T S X E W
V E B S A M I R R O R H P A T N P N P V
M S N L Y O H R X F B Y F K I P E M P S
K S O O B A Z T Y E R O T G U G Y H I M
K Z O S I C E J S O O J K L W T W A L D
X Y P F P T M N Z L W E E D W Y G R C N
V D X O Z H O N G E V P O X V H Q P L B
R M V I V Z Q L E C E V F D S S O C I K
R T E N I B A C E N I C I D E M C C A L
C G Z V L A V A T O R Y E C A I N Y N F
```

Word List

LAUNDRY HAMPER	LAVATORY	LOOFAH
LOTION	MAKE UP	MEDICATIONS
MEDICINE	MEDICINE CABINET	MIRROR
MOISTURIZER	MOUTHWASH	NAIL CLIPPERS

What's brown and spins around your waist? *A hula poop.*

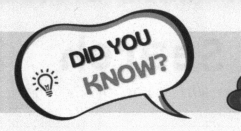

A fart is just a secret your butt whispers to your underwear.

Connect the Plops

Just remember, every dot (and toot) counts!

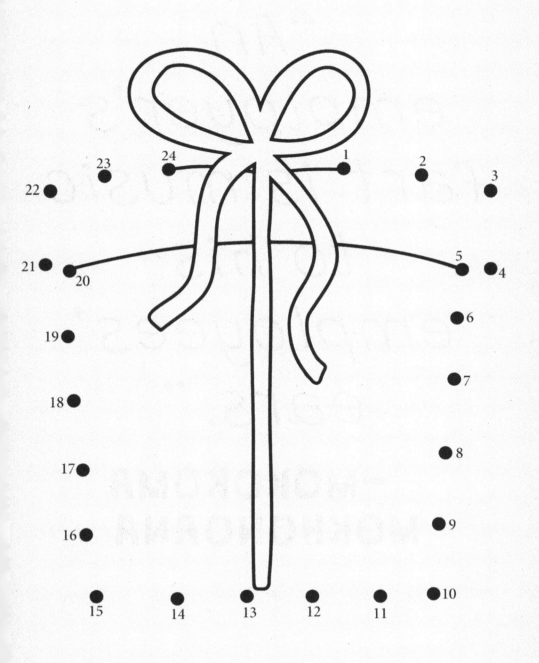

"An employer's fart is music to his employees' ears."

–MOKOKOMA MOKHONOANA

Word Scramble

Brain While You Drain

Did you hear about the boy who couldn't stop farting in   class?

He was a-gassed!

STOP DEPRESSION

DMSIAY ☐☐☐☐☐☐

KOCN ☐☐☐☐

USNSI ☐☐☐☐☐

RPCAS ☐☐☐☐☐

EELTTK ☐☐☐☐☐☐

SKEDSANR ☐☐☐☐☐☐☐☐

DONPETUSP ☐☐☐☐☐☐☐☐☐

YRTAR ☐☐☐☐☐

EORASCSYC ☐☐☐☐☐☐☐☐☐

AQCETUDU ☐☐☐☐☐☐☐☐

SSIRFEU ☐☐☐☐☐☐☐

CAINM ☐☐☐☐☐

KNOCK KNOCK! JOKES

Knock-knock!
Who's there?
Justin.
Justin who?

*Justin time to make it to the bathroom, whew!
You stink!*

Knock-knock!
Who's there?
Harry.
Harry who?

*Harry up, I need to get to
the toilet!*

How does a cow's fart smell?

Udderly terrible.

Help The Farting Cow Get to The Toilet

Some-times, You have to Go back to square one

Word Search

Brain While You Drain

```
N L E W O T R E P A P N F G R E F P L P
L W V D D S V J S H E E H S I I W T O J
U Q U I L C C I F B H V G L S O V L K C
P P X D X S P R O Q D R E G N U L P I L
F L R Y P T G Z Y Z A B W R F T A O E X
P G N I F A H U T N S G N I B M U L P C
P Z T A J J W T O W K Q I C U H D Y W Z
J Q B N I D P A H Z C N W S J F V H K G
V E S V E L M N Y J U R C J O I C Q R R
Y I X I V M S D Z W P R A Z O R M A N M
F B N G K I T C B A G C E Y L M Z F E N
U P A K P V L N I D T X L H S O W Q Z A
Z K I X O A P Q I S I F L X R I P C A I
R B L O C Y O X D O S P S B V Q Q Q X L
C X P E Q A W K U F E O L F I V X R K F
J J O H O Z D A H R O A R U P A Z I L I
K R L X E D E N F L D K A S R O O A I L
H V I B Y F R U G E U E A A G G K S I E
E T S C J Y M I Y I W X B H L D P R N K
Y Y H B I E Z N U A U O V G H G Z W U D
```

Word List

NAIL FILE	NAIL POLISH	NAIL SCISSORS
OINTMENT	PAPER TOWEL	PERFUME
PLUMBING	PLUNGER	POWDER
Q TIPS	RAZOR	RAZOR BLADE

What do the poets do in the bathroom? *They write poo-ems.*

Farting is just your butt being jealous of your talking, singing mouth.

Sudok-Poo!

Ensuring no 'number repeats' in this gassy grid

							1		7
			4	9	7				
	5				3				4
					5	8	2		
	8	5	3						
	4		8	7	6		5		
4			5				6		
			9	3	4				
1	3								

What's worse than finding a fly in your soup?

Finding a fly in your poop.

odd tidbits from the world of bathrooms

Toilet Paper Crisis: *In 1973, there was a false rumor of a toilet paper shortage in the US. Johnny Carson made a joke about it on "The Tonight Show," and the next day, stores really did run out of stock because everyone panicked and hoarded toilet paper!*

Musical Manners: *There's a term for the embarrassment of making noise in a public restroom: "paruresis." In Japan, to combat this, some toilets play a flushing sound to mask any... er, incidental noises. No more awkward silences!*

World Record: *The world's longest toilet roll was created in 2001 and measured 2.15 miles long. Imagine if that accidentally unraveled in your bathroom!*

Historical Humor: *The ancient Romans had multi-seat public toilets with no dividers — making it a very social affair. Imagine chatting about the latest chariot race while, well, you know...*

Presidential Potty: *U.S. President Lyndon B. Johnson had a habit of taking people into his bathroom during discussions. Talk about bathroom diplomacy!*

Word Scramble

Brain While You Drain

What do you call a little zit?
A simple pimple.

SIMPLE LIVING

ELGINS   ☐☐☐☐☐☐

CHTNA   ☐☐☐☐☐

CNENATI   ☐☐☐☐☐☐☐

TEADNFFUEC   ☐☐☐☐☐☐☐☐☐☐

SCLIPTIIYM   ☐☐☐☐☐☐☐☐☐☐

TLSREIE   ☐☐☐☐☐☐☐

ADFT   ☐☐☐☐

OIPNLTMES   ☐☐☐☐☐☐☐☐☐

SATRGEEND   ☐☐☐☐☐☐☐☐☐

LAIOGLOCIB   ☐☐☐☐☐☐☐☐☐☐

NOIPSNLAG   ☐☐☐☐☐☐☐☐☐

CAELP   ☐☐☐☐☐

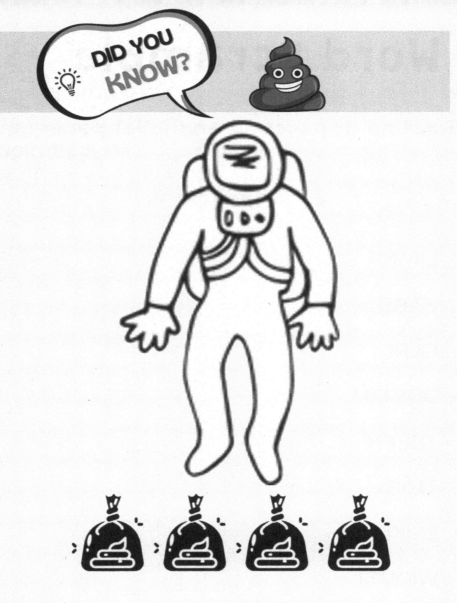

There are 4 Bags of
Neil Armtrong's
Poop on The Moon

Word Scramble

What do a spaceship and toilet paper have in common?

They both probe Uranus.

PAPER CRAFT

LKANB   ☐☐☐☐☐

CARD   ☐☐☐☐

OLRL   ☐☐☐☐

UDIMEM   ☐☐☐☐☐☐

TSEEH   ☐☐☐☐☐

TMIE   ☐☐☐☐

LSIKL   ☐☐☐☐☐

WIOUTT   ☐☐☐☐☐☐

AEPT   ☐☐☐☐

ESVTA   ☐☐☐☐☐

ETLHANEP   ☐☐☐☐☐☐☐☐

LPHTMAPE   ☐☐☐☐☐☐☐☐

Farting is a literal example of somebody butting into the conversation.

Word Search

Brain While You Drain

```
T V T A T S T O W L O A L Z W S M D D Q
N G J O G H P D B G G S F R J W S Q P H
P J N L T A M F B R Z B D S U H Z F N Y
H V P E C V D B J E J O X O O G Z P K L
S C L B P E Z X B W U V W W Q F O B W T
D H A T O H M E Y O J Y E E C B P W C D
N M O E G J Y Q Q H I R V S H A M P O O
O F X W Q K I K P S C Z J Z U M H X L N
U W V K E J S F T U U T S E L X G N A C
A V L M O R Y X R A P V B I X H F H I V
H A G O U A S T X S K F R D N G A L H P
P S G O J A A T C M H F A G T K Y D H Z
D Z I R T I K E A S R O S S I C S S M P
I J Z T N S G W J L N N J B U D L Z M N
Q P Y S E C E B I T L T A D S D V O D E
R G A E F A R S T W R K I H B K O B E N
O I I R C L L T M R M P A H I T Z Z R Z
C M U Z M E K V Z L F V I J S O X L U N
Z S H A V I N G C R E A M Y P S I U S L
U S R G B N S Y D R G W L T H O U Z M I
```

Word List

RESTROOM	RUG	SCALE
SCISSORS	SHAMPOO	SHAVE
SHAVER	SHAVING CREAM	SHOWER
SHOWER CURTAIN	SHOWER STALL	SINK

What's the most disgusting kids' book ever written? *Diarrhea of a Wimpy Kid.*

Pooping is just having one last goodbye with a meal you truly loved.

Word Scramble

Brain While You Drain

What does a competitive eater do in the bathroom?

Prepare for battle.

SLOW DOWN

OUSSE ⬜⬜⬜⬜⬜

ARGTNES ⬜⬜⬜⬜⬜⬜⬜

RUODUSHNOE ⬜⬜⬜⬜⬜⬜⬜⬜⬜⬜

EPNDED ⬜⬜⬜⬜⬜⬜

LILK ⬜⬜⬜⬜

RDWA ⬜⬜⬜⬜

USTCTROB ⬜⬜⬜⬜⬜⬜⬜⬜

BDILREB ⬜⬜⬜⬜⬜⬜⬜

ARYRT ⬜⬜⬜⬜⬜

DENRU ⬜⬜⬜⬜⬜

NYNAC ⬜⬜⬜⬜⬜

LETACEDERE ⬜⬜⬜⬜⬜⬜⬜⬜⬜⬜

KNOCK KNOCK! JOKES

Knock-knock!
Who's there?

Dwayne.
Dwayne who?

Dwayne the tub; I need to use the toilet!

Knock-knock!
Who's there?
Dismay.
Dismay who?

Dismay be the last time I'll let you use my toilet.

Word Search

Brain While You Drain

```
T X U M V J G V N W Y I A S H K C A M S
O Y E R I C U G N A A S X B Q O V Q I X
E W D T I E G I R A J T S B H O A R D C
E E X T C N S X J A W Z E N P N E R K U
H B B M O A A M B J X R A R L S T U B X
W U W T B W T L T Q D W X Z R A T R C O
S M L H O J E C J Q S W U E K E F G T B
R R S W S W D L R S V B Z K K A E G X J
Q A C J Z B E T Z M Q E A S E V E S D H
W W A T E R C L O S E T A N E Q S L H D
O R A Q U V N M R W B B N A C H S A R T
A M M N E P W H T A E L E V P V I O D V
V D Q X J B S A O T C I K B B Z J G Y Z
N O Y J Q B N F S K C K N B J Y A C S Z
Y M F E U H F A C H E Q E L Z X G O W B
D L F W M U W B J E R F A S Y O Z Q W Y
S V P C T Y O R R X Q O W T G Z A O H L
H P N Y U S V E S G M T O H W Q V W B F
V S A L D N I R J C Z K U M W K W O E M
V Y V X B T C K Y O J C S I Q C M X Q F
```

Word List

ASH	TOWEL	TOWEL RACK
TRASH CAN	TUB	TWEEZERS
URINAL	WASH BASIN	WASHROOM
WASTEBASKET	WATER	WATER CLOSET

What are grizzly bear farts like?
Silent but violent.

Pandas Can Poop Up to 48 Pounds Per Day

Word Search

Brain While You Drain

```
M M G G C M A F B E T F L A M Y K U O H
D H E C E M E Y S Z M E U Z Q L E U V P
H W M T E R B Q B Q W J T H K E Y A C Y
A I E H W K O L D O G Y B T X L G S S S
I F R Y G V A H T L C X J Y E J W I Z F
R S Y U O A H D A C W C W Z W C W Y P L
B T B H G D N K A I H C U Z K R U S V U
R B O W R A R J C J R Y X T D N X A X S
U H A I H R G Y S Y B D E N R D Q G F H
S C R F X G C X G A E I R R R G P U P F
H F D X V X V N B Z D E E Y F F X R E A
V Q N X S E C O I M Q P S F E Q U H T C
Z U V S N U F X G G P S Q X T F R J D J E
R K O B G U J U O O L R E P M A H C Z C
J L Q H F R A Z R F H F L K N N O M Q L
F N L W M X K D N G O Y H L A O L J Q O
U K N C I M E V Z S D F J T C B J Z R T
G X V P U Y P Q O Q I Y W C F L Z M T H
A D X D E M T R P H N A C E G A B R A G
T Z W W J H J U X A G D S R F Y V Z E L
```

Word List

DRY	EMERY BOARD	EYEDROPPER
FACE CLOTH	FAUCET	FLOSS
FLUSH	GARBAGE CAN	HAIR DRYER
HAIRBRUSH	HAMPER	HAND TOWEL

What does bear poop smell like?

Unbearable.

Farting is just your body making thunder before the lightning.

FAMOUS FARTY QUOTES

"You failed—your fart was not silent, my nose heard its deafening noise."

—ANIEKEE TOCHUKWU EZEKIEL

Word Scramble

Brain While You Drain

What did the guy get when he couldn't make it to the bathroom in time?

Heavy pants.

VALUE OF TIME

EOCINOMC   ☐☐☐☐☐☐☐☐

BTALEAR   ☐☐☐☐☐☐☐

TNIU   ☐☐☐☐

NRBAER   ☐☐☐☐☐☐

OORP   ☐☐☐☐

NNICTNUECAO   ☐☐☐☐☐☐☐☐☐☐☐

MARIRPY   ☐☐☐☐☐☐☐

ANERTIPOTU   ☐☐☐☐☐☐☐☐☐☐

OSHOK   ☐☐☐☐☐

SUHBIYBR   ☐☐☐☐☐☐☐☐

AVIN   ☐☐☐☐

SLUEPETTX   ☐☐☐☐☐☐☐☐☐

SHIT'S ABOUT
TO GO
Down

ROLLIN WITH THE HOMIES

What is the stinkiest day of the week?
Tootsday.

Help The Farting Monkey Get to
The Toilet *(before he poops on himself)*

KNOCK KNOCK! JOKES

Knock-knock!
Who's there?
A pileup.
A pileup who?

A pileup poo in the toilet?
You better flush!

Knock-knock!
Who's there?
Russian.
Russian who?

Russian to the bathroom!

Sudok-Poo!

							4.	5
			4		7			9
4	8						7	
	8			5				1
						6	2	
6		7	2	9				4
						3		6
	6			8			5	
1		3	5	7			8	

What can go right through your pants and not leave a hole?

A fart.

Be soft on people they'll appreciate it in the End.

Why did the boy fart in the cemetery?
Because he read a tombstone that said RIP.

Help The Stinkbug Get To The Toilet

(before he poops on himself)

If you have a problem to solve, put your whole self into it.

Why did the turkey need a bath?
It smelled fowl.

Help the Tissue Get to The Butt

KNOCK KNOCK! JOKES

Knock-knock!
Who's there?
Rhino.
Rhino who?

Rhino you're the one who farted.

If you're an odious gas, life begins at farty.

Knock-knock!
Who's there?
Omar.
Omar who?

Omar goodness, these farts are horrible!

What bathroom item is the biggest rip-off?
Toilet paper.

Help The Tissue Get to The Butt

"*My trumpeting sounds like a goose farting in the fog.*"

— ALEX O'LOUGHLIN

What do you call a comedian with irritable bowel syndrome?

The life of the potty.

Get the toilet papper to the butt!

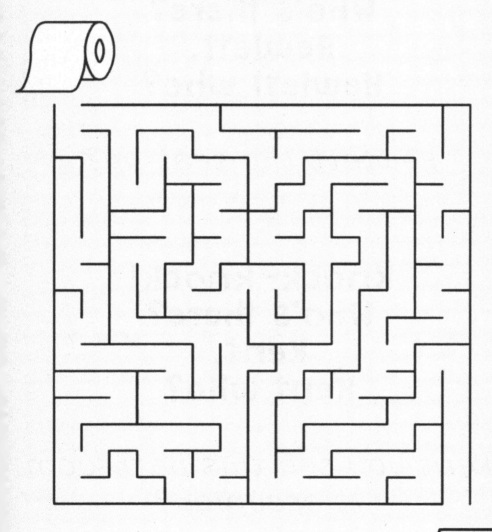

KNOCK KNOCK! JOKES

Knock-knock!
Who's there?
Hewlett.
Hewlett who?

Hewlett the seat up?

Knock-knock!
Who's there?
Kent.
Kent who?

Kent you see this bathroom is occupied?

Sudok-Poo!

	7						4	
8				7				
4	9	1	2			3		
7	1		8	3				
6	4		1		2			8
				5	7			4
3	8					2	1	
					1		8	3
1	6				8	4		7

What do you call a bathroom in Finland?

Helstinki.

When is the most satisfying time to go to the bathroom?
Poo thirty!

Have a nice 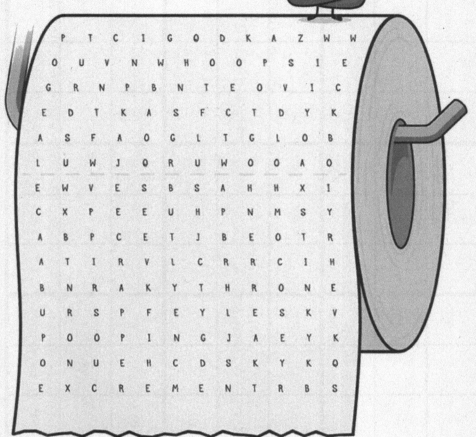!

```
P  T  C  I  G  O  D  K  A  Z  W  W
O  U  V  N  W  H  O  O  P  S  I  E
G  R  N  P  B  N  T  E  O  V  I  C
E  D  T  K  A  S  F  C  T  D  Y  K
A  S  F  A  O  G  L  T  G  L  O  B
L  U  W  J  Q  R  U  W  O  O  A  O
E  W  V  E  S  B  S  A  H  H  X  I
C  X  P  E  E  U  H  P  N  M  S  Y
A  B  P  C  E  T  J  B  E  O  T  R
A  T  I  R  V  L  C  R  R  C  I  H
B  N  R  A  K  Y  T  H  R  O  N  E
U  R  S  P  F  E  Y  L  E  S  K  V
P  O  O  P  I  N  G  J  A  E  Y  K
O  N  U  E  H  C  D  S  K  Y  K  Q
E  X  C  R  E  M  E  N  T  R  B  S
```

POOPING	THRONE	FLUSH
EXCREMENT	TURDS	DOO-DOO
STINKY	SWEET CHEEKS	WHOOPSIE
GUANO	CRAPPER	NICE BUTT

...and don't forget to flush.

"*Home is where the heart is, home is where the fart is.*"

—ERNEST HEMINGWAY

Sudok-Poo!

Ensuring no 'number repeats' in this gassy grid

					8			
	5		1	9				8
8		2	6	7			1	
			5					
	6			8	7			1
4				6	1	7	5	
6					2		8	
5			9				7	
9		7		5		1	6	

What's worse than smelling a fart?

Tasting one.

KNOCK KNOCK! JOKES

Knock-knock!
Who's there?
Who.
Who who?

Who flushed that poor owl down the toilet? I can hear it from here!

Knock-knock!
Who's there?
Candy.
Candy who?

Candy farting please stop now?

Sudok-Poo!

Ensuring no 'number repeats' in this gassy grid

	2		9		5	4	6	
6				2		5	3	
		7	4		3			9
			3				9	
4	5	9			2	3		
	3				4			
2	6	5			1	9		
			5				2	
	4					7		

What's the smelliest retail store?

Walfart.

When You Feel Completely wiped out, remember, tomorrow's is a brand new Day.

Sudok-Poo!

4	6			1			3	2
3	8					9	1	
			4		7			8
6	3		4	8				1
				9	1			3
1	9		2		3			
	1					8		
5	4	3	9				2	
8					4			

Why did the woman pass gas in the elevator?

She wanted to take her farts to a new level.

bathroom

[bath-ruhm] **noun.**
a temporary sanctuary for overwhelmed parents seeking refuge from their offspring.

What's the stinkiest city? Pitts-burgh.

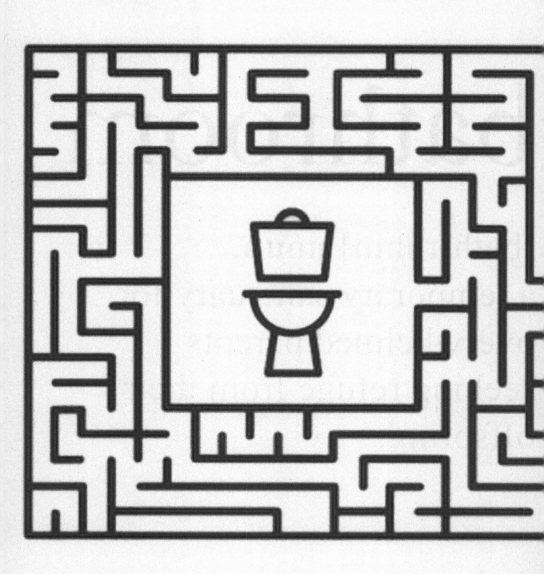

"You are all made of real poop."

–ANNE FRANK

Poop Guestbook

where every 'deposit' gets a cheeky shout-out!

☁ First name and last name of the guest:

_____

☁ How do you know the host?

_____

☁ favorite pastime while pooping:

_____

Let's agree

Comfort water [1][2][3][4][5][6][7][8][9][10]

Hygiene [1][2][3][4][5][6][7][8][9][10]

Bend [1][2][3][4][5][6][7][8][9][10]

Quality toilet paper [1][2][3][4][5][6][7][8][9][10]

General experience [1][2][3][4][5][6][7][8][9][10]

☁ Describe how you felt after that poop:

_____

_____

_____

☁ Suggestions for improving service:

_____

_____

Poop Guestbook

where every 'deposit' gets a cheeky shout-out!

☁ Give this defecatory act
a title:

_____

☁ Last meal eaten:

_____

Weight: _____

Length: _____

Draw your own poop:

probability of death of those who
occur later:

0% ⊂⎯⎯⎯⎯⎯⎯⎯⎯⎯⎯⎯⊃ 100%

Date

_____

Signature

_____

Sudok-Poo!
Solutions

Word Search

Solutions

Bathroom Word Search 1

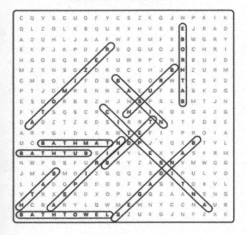

Bathroom Word Search 2

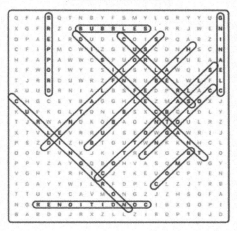

Bathroom Word Search 3

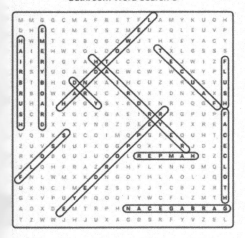

Bathroom Word Search 4

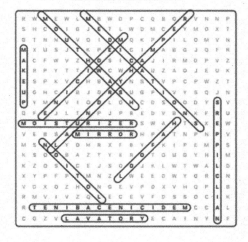

Word Search

Solutions

Bathroom Word Search 5

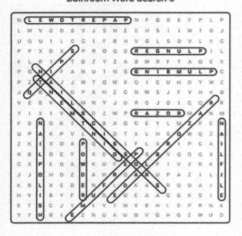

Bathroom Word Search 6

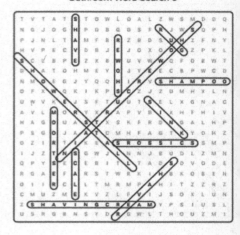

Bathroom Word Search 7

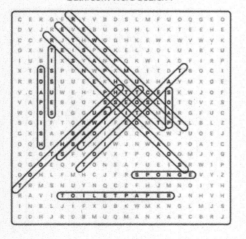

Bathroom Word Search 8

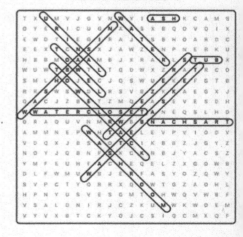

Milton Keynes UK
Ingram Content Group UK Ltd.
UKHW041307201123
432918UK00009B/101